A START UP

1. 65p ÷ 5 = [ ] p

2. [kg] – 13kg = 14kg

3. (3km + [km]) × 6 = 72km

4. £90 × [ ] = £400 + £50

5. [ ] = ½ of 23

6. [litres] = 9 litres × 6

7. (4 + 31 + 13) ÷ 4 = [ ]

8. 4 × 14 = [ ] + 50

9. 35 + 29 = [ ] + 32

10. ¾ + ½ + ¼ = [ ]

11. 1.5 – 0.7 – 0.3 = [ ]

12. [ ] × 5 × 4 = 100

13. 40mm × [ ] = 8cm

14. [m] ÷ 4 = 17m

15. 35hrs + [hrs] = 2 days

16. ²⁄₅ – ¹⁄₁₀ = [ ] tenths

Marks [ ]

B INTO GEAR

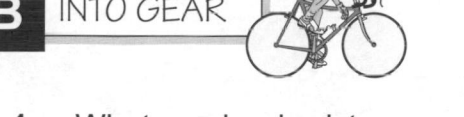

1. What number is sixteen more than 39? [ ]

2. What is the product of three, four and five? [ ]

3. Divide 56 by four and multiply the answer by five. [ ]

4. 41 is how many more than 24? [ ]

5. Round these numbers to the nearest hundred:

2754 [ ] 3639 [ ] 5051 [ ]

6. Share eighteen items equally among six people. How many items each? [ ]

Marks [ ]

C TOUGH CHALLENGE

1. Which 4 coins together make 47p? [ ] p [ ] p [ ] p [ ] p

2. Caroline spent 30 minutes each day, Monday to Saturday, on her paper round.
   How many hours is this? [ ] hrs

3. Which 3 coins are given in change from £7 after spending £6.25? [ ] p [ ] p [ ] p

4. A bottle of lemonade makes 6 drinks. How many drinks will 11 bottles make? [ ] drinks

5. Write in words the number that is a hundred and fifty times the size of 10.

[ ]

Marks [ ]

A START UP

1. $26p + 15p + 9p =$ ☐ p

2. ☐ kg $- 29kg = 19kg$

3. $8cm \times$ ☐ $= 48cm \div 2$

4. $\frac{5}{10} = 0.5$ so $\frac{7}{10} =$ ☐

5. ☐ g $+ 15g = 53g$

6. $50 -$ ☐ $- 17 = 21$

7. $600 + 600 + 500 =$ ☐

8. 1330, 1230, ☐ , 1030

9. $49 \times 2 \times$ ☐ $= 196$

10. ☐ km $\div 2 = 0.4km$

11. £4.20 + £6.50 = £☐

12. $41 - 16 -$ ☐ $= 15$

13. 48, ☐ , 58, 63, 68

14. (☐ ml $\times 3) \div 2 = 21ml$

15. $42g -$ ☐ g $- 7g = 10g$

16. $\frac{2}{4} + \frac{1}{2} + \frac{3}{4} + \frac{5}{10} =$ ☐

Marks

B INTO GEAR

1. Find the total of 22 and 19. ☐

2. Find the difference between 45 and 27. ☐

3. What number is five times more than nineteen? ☐

4. How many is a fifth of 100? ☐

5. Which number is 6 times greater than ten? ☐

6. Decrease 5000 by 450. ☐

7. Increase 350 by 1000 and then by 70. ☐

Marks

C TOUGH CHALLENGE

1. How much greater is the distance round a rectangle measuring 15cm by 6cm than the distance round a rectangle measuring 3cm by 16cm? ☐ cm

2. 4 items of equal weight have a total mass of 84g.

   What is the mass of 3 items? ☐ g

3. $\frac{1}{5}$ of my money is 17p. What is my total amount? ☐ p

4. A half kilogram of pears costs 32p.

   What will be the cost of a quarter kilogram? ☐ p

Marks

A START UP

1. $(72km \div 4) \times 5 =$ ☐ km
2. $(19 \times$ ☐ $) + 4 + 5 = 85$
3. ☐ kg $- 29kg = 9kg$
4. $1.25m + 4.75m =$ ☐ cm
5. ☐ g $+ 36g = 54g$
6. $(37 - 21 - 7) \div 3 =$ ☐
7. $8cm \times$ ☐ $= 48cm$
8. $\frac{1}{5}$ of 70 litres = ☐ litres

9. $42p + 42p + 8p =$ ☐ p
10. $2.9m - 1.8m =$ ☐ m
11. $41 \div 2 = \frac{1}{2} +$ ☐
12. ☐ mm $= 16mm \times 5$
13. $(42 \div 3) + (36 - 19) =$ ☐
14. $3.6 + 1.4 + 2.3 =$ ☐
15. $37hrs -$ ☐ hrs $= 15hrs$
16. $\frac{1}{2} + \frac{2}{4} - \frac{3}{6} + \frac{5}{10} =$ ☐

Marks ☐

B INTO GEAR

1. Half of 96 divided by two. ☐

2. Round these numbers to the nearest 1000:

   2568 ☐   5992 ☐   9499 ☐   4770 ☐

3. Add the odd numbers between 12 and 18. ☐

4. From 330 subtract sixty. ☐

5. What is the remainder when 5 is shared into 49? ☐

6. Give the number that is 100 more than 219 + 60. ☐

Marks ☐

C TOUGH CHALLENGE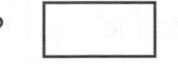

1. Jenna is 9 years old. Her grandmother is 56 years old.

   How old was her grandmother when Jenna was born? ☐

2. Mr. Holmes is 48 years older than his grandson. His grandson is 13 years old.

   What age is Mr. Holmes? ☐

3. 93 labels were put into packets of 3. How many packets would there be? ☐

4. Which 3 coins are given in change from £6 after spending £5.25? ☐ p ☐ p ☐ p

5. To the sum of 6 and 6 add the product of 6 and 6. ☐

Marks ☐

A START UP

1. $1.30m + 2.45m = \boxed{}$ m

2. $\boxed{}$ kg $- 14kg = 24kg$

3. $-6 + 12 + 16 + 18 = \boxed{}$

4. £1.50 $+ \boxed{£ } = £9.00$

5. $27km \div \boxed{} = 4\frac{1}{2}km \times 2$

6. $\boxed{ \text{litres}} = 16$ litres $\times 4$

7. $(27 + 38) \div \boxed{} = 13$

8. $90 \div 6 \div 5 = 30 - \boxed{}$

9. $\boxed{ mm} + 49mm = 67mm$

10. $5 \times (33 - 16) = \boxed{}$

11. $41ml + \boxed{ ml} = 63ml$

12. $(\boxed{} + 17) \div 3 = 16$

13. $1\frac{1}{2} + \frac{3}{4} = \boxed{}$ quarters

14. $(6 \times 4 \times 4) \div 6 = \boxed{}$

15. $\boxed{} = 42 - (64 \div 4)$

16. Take 15g from 39g. $\boxed{ g}$

Marks

B INTO GEAR

1. What number is 27 more than twenty-six? $\boxed{}$

2. How many times less than fifty is 5? $\boxed{}$

3. Work out $\frac{1}{6}$ of 24. $\boxed{}$

4. Find the total of forty-nine, thirty-two and seven. $\boxed{}$

5. Ten times three multiplied by three is how many? $\boxed{}$

6. From 46 subtract thirty-four. $\boxed{}$

7. Write down the number that is 6 times larger than 6. $\boxed{}$

Marks

C TOUGH CHALLENGE

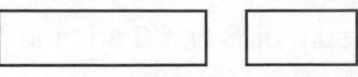

1. Add together 19 cups, 37 cups and 6 cups. $\boxed{ \text{cups}}$

2. Anthony went to the zoo at 9.30 a.m. He ate his lunch 3½ hours later.
   At what time did he have his lunch? $\boxed{ \text{p.m.}}$

3. A train travels at 80 kph. How far does it travel in 15 mins? $\boxed{ km}$

4. A purse held 3 FIVES and 6 TWENTIES. How much less than £2.00 was this? $\boxed{ p}$

5. Sam's marbles equal ¼ of 32. Sue's marbles equal $\frac{1}{3}$ of 27.
   Who has the most marbles and by how many? $\boxed{}$ $\boxed{}$

Marks

A START UP

1. $4 \times 5\frac{1}{4}$ litres = [   ] litres

2. $26 - 12 - 3 + 34 =$ [   ]

3. $\frac{1}{3}$ of $90 =$ [   ] $\times 5$

4. $\frac{1}{2}$ of $25km =$ [   ] km

5. [   ] $- 1.3 - 2.4 = 0.8$

6. $65 = (2 \times$ [   ] $\times 2) + 1$

7. [   ] , 191, 197, 203

8. [   ] $m + 16m - 6m = 58m$

9. $£11.00 \div 2 = £$ [   ]

10. $\frac{3}{10}$ of $80cm =$ [   ] cm

11. $26hrs +$ [   ] hrs $= 2$ days

12. ([   ] $\times 5) + 5 = 60$

13. $48g \div 4 = 60g \div$ [   ]

14. [   ] $= \frac{1}{2}$ of 33

15. $36 -$ [   ] $- 4 - 5 = 10$

16. 4 fifths = 8 [   ]

Marks [   ]

B INTO GEAR

1. Find the product of 2, 12 and 3. [   ]

2. Make one hundred and forty 6 times as large. [   ]

3. Divide fifty by two and your answer by five. [   ]

4. Round these numbers to the nearest 1000:

   3005 [   ]   5505 [   ]   9050 [   ]   7855 [   ]

5. Add together fifty and thirty-eight and subtract your total from one hundred. [   ]

6. Increase forty-seven by thirty. [   ]

Marks [   ]

C TOUGH CHALLENGE

1. If a $\frac{1}{2}$ kilogram of beef costs £1.60 work out the cost of $\frac{3}{4}$ of a kilogram. £ [   ]

2. The weight of 3 different pencils is 50g, 30g and 40g.

   Work out their average weight. [   ] g

3. 6 of Victoria's paces measure 420cm.

   What is the length of one of her paces? [   ] cm

4. At the school Sports Day there were 200 children. $\frac{3}{5}$ of them were boys.

   How many were girls? [   ]

Marks [   ]

5

A START UP

1. ½ *of* 31 = ☐

2. − 7 + ☐ = 40 + 3 + 27

3. (45*p* + ☐ *p*) ÷ 3 = 24*p*

4. ¹⁴⁄₄ = ☐ *halves*

5. ☐ *m* − 21*m* = 9*m* + 9*m*

6. ☐ *min* × 9 = 45*min*

7. (1.4 × 6) ÷ 2 = 3.1 + ☐

8. (85 ÷ 5) × (13 − 9) = ☐

9. 46 − 7 + 3 − 8 = ☐ − 3

10. 49*g* − 15*g* + 24*g* = ☐ *g*

11. 18*ml* + ☐ *ml* = 62*ml*

12. 0.5 + 2 = ☐ *quarters*

13. Twice 37 = 150 − ☐

14. 21 + 38 − 5 + 3 = ☐

15. ☐ ÷ 5 = 15

16. ⅓ *of* 60 = 37 − ☐

Marks ☐

B INTO GEAR

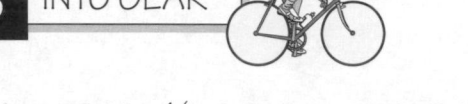

1. Divide ⅓ of 96 by a half of four. ☐

2. Write in words the smallest 3-digit number you can make from the figures 9, 7 and 1.

☐

3. Write in words the largest 3-digit number you can make from the figures 5, 7 and 9.

☐

4. Decrease forty-five by twenty-nine. ☐

5. Add 35 to 36 and subtract your answer from 80. ☐

Marks ☐

C TOUGH CHALLENGE

1. An equilateral triange has a side of 7cm. ☐ cm

   What is the total distance in centimetres twice round the perimeter of the shape?

2. How many days altogether in March, June and October? ☐ days

3. What fraction of a metre is: 60cm? ☐   75cm? ☐

4. Add together these amounts of money: £0.23   18p   36p ☐ p

5. Six pieces of string each measure 50cm.

   What is their total length in metres? ☐ m

Marks ☐

A START UP

1. 27 *litres* ÷ 2 = ⬚ litres

2. ⬚ ml − 21*ml* = 26*ml*

3. 2.8 + 1.4 + 0.9 = ⬚

4. *Multiply* 27 *by* 3. ⬚

5. ⬚ min × 6 = 78*min*

6. 17*p* + ⬚ p + 4*p* = 65*p*

7. ($\frac{2}{3}$ of 9) × (12 + 8) = ⬚

8. 41 − 27 = ⬚ + 3 + 7

9. 90*cm* ÷ 5 = ⬚ cm

10. 26*cm* + 39*cm* = ⬚ cm

11. ⬚ = 80 ÷ 5 ÷ 4

12. $\frac{1}{6}$ of 78 + $\frac{1}{3}$ of 9 = ⬚

13. 3*ml* × ⬚ = 93*ml*

14. ¾ of 44 = ⬚ − 16

15. 5*km* × ⬚ = 100*km*

16. 127, 131, ⬚ , 139, ⬚

Marks ⬚

B INTO GEAR

1. Multiply a sixth of sixty-six by a half of ten. ⬚

2. Subtract fifteen from 24 and times the answer by 3. ⬚

3. What number is four times larger than twelve? ⬚

4. How many do you add to each of these numbers to make 100?

   73 ⬚   41 ⬚   38 ⬚   65 ⬚   29 ⬚   14 ⬚

5. Multiply treble six by nothing. ⬚

6. How many sixes have the same value as sixty? ⬚

Marks ⬚

C TOUGH CHALLENGE

1. When 34 pins are subtracted from 49 pins how many pins are left? ⬚ pins

2. Total up the numbers of months in five years. ⬚ months

3. How many FIVES have the same value as the sum of 32p and £0.18? ⬚

4. How many cm are there in 2¼ metres? ⬚ cm

5. ¾ of a number is 27. What is the number? ⬚

6. If it costs 30p to travel 6km how much will it cost to travel 8km at the same rate? ⬚ p

Marks ⬚

7

A START UP

1. ½ of 39 *litres* = ☐ *litres*

2. 0.6, 1.1, ☐, 2.1, 2.6

3. 10*min* × ☐ = 2 *hours*

4. 50 − 3 − 5 − 7 − 9 = ☐

5. 5 × (33 − 16) = ☐

6. ☐ *km* = 33*km* − 25*km*

7. ☐ = (76 ÷ 4) × 3

8. 34*ml* + 48*ml* = ☐ *ml*

9. 9 + 31 = 8 × ☐ = 10 × 4

10. 24½ = ½ of ☐

11. 902, ☐, 896, 893, 890

12. 45*m* − 17*m* − 6*m* = ☐ *m*

13. − 5 + ☐ = 23 + 34

14. (☐ ÷ 3) × 2 = 34

15. 37*ml* + ☐ *ml* = 77*ml*

16. 6 × (31 − 18) = ☐

Marks ☐

B INTO GEAR

1. How many sets of three in forty-five? ☐

2. Add twenty-nine and thirteen. ☐

3. Find the total of thirty-four and sixteen. ☐

4. What is the product of twenty-two and four? ☐

5. Round these numbers to the nearest 10:

   166 ☐   429 ☐   811 ☐   634 ☐   372 ☐

6. From twice 14 subtract fifteen. ☐

Marks ☐

C TOUGH CHALLENGE

1. What is the cost of 15 items at 5p each? ☐ p

2. Work out the distance round a square with a side of 13cm. ☐ cm

3. How much less is ⅕ of £65.00 than ¼ of £80.00? £ ☐

4. Three small chocolate bars cost 51p. How many bars could be bought for £0.68?

5. What must be added to £0.34 to equal £0.73? £ ☐   ☐ bars

6. Lynsey has 24p and Hayley has half as much as Lynsey.

   How much have the two girls altogether? ☐ p

Marks ☐

A START UP

1. $21 \times 2 = 7 \times \boxed{}$

2. $\boxed{} = (12 \div 6) \times 15$

3. $32 - \boxed{} = 8 + 11$

4. ½ of $66m = 18m + \boxed{}$ m

5. $\boxed{}$, 69, 64, 59, 54, $\boxed{}$

6. $16g + 28g - 12g = \boxed{}$ g

7. 3 *months* $\times \boxed{} = 3$ *years*

8. $(£39 \div 3) \times 2 = £\boxed{}$

9. $54 \div \boxed{} = 33 - 15$

10. $38hrs - 19hrs = \boxed{}$ hrs

11. ½ of $37kg = \boxed{}$ kg

12. 2470, 2370, $\boxed{}$, 2170

13. $\boxed{} \div 6 = 7 \times 2$

14. 426, 416, $\boxed{}$, 396, $\boxed{}$

15. $1.9m \times 2 = \boxed{}$ cm

16. $9mm \times 4 = \boxed{} \times 3mm$

Marks

B INTO GEAR

1. 32 multiplied by 3. $\boxed{}$

2. Total up all the single-digit numbers and subtract from 100. $\boxed{}$

3. From fifty take twenty-five and seventeen. $\boxed{}$

4. How many is ¼ of sixty? $\boxed{}$

5. 74, 68, $\boxed{}$, 56, 50, $\boxed{}$, $\boxed{}$, 32, $\boxed{}$, 20, 14, $\boxed{}$

6. Find the sum of 21, 23 and thirteen. $\boxed{}$

7. Add fifty to twenty-two plus twelve. $\boxed{}$

Marks

C TOUGH CHALLENGE

1. Which two amounts of the following four add up to £41.00?

   £25.00, £31.00, £18.00, £16.00 $£\boxed{}$ $£\boxed{}$

2. Three items were bought costing 23p, 12p and 8p.

   Write down the 2 largest value coins that could be given in change from a FIFTY. $\boxed{}$ p $\boxed{}$ p

3. A jar contained 100g of sweetener. 45g were used.

   How many grams of sweetener were left? $\boxed{}$ g

4. How many miles will be travelled in 9 hours at 60mph? $\boxed{}$ miles

Marks

A START UP

1. ⅔ *of* 24 *litres* = [ ] litres

2. 2.1 + 0.9 = [ ] − 1.9

3. − 8 + 17 + 6 + 11 = [ ]

4. [ ] = 45 − 5 − 6 − 7

5. 17*ml* + 16*ml* = [ ] ml

6. 65 = (2 × 2 × [ ]) + 1

7. 6 *sixths* = [ ] *thirds*

8. 72*hrs* ÷ 4 = 47*hrs* − [ ] hrs

9. [ ] km = 18*km* + 19*km*

10. 13 *days* × 5 = [ ] days

11. 92, [ ], 84, 80, [ ]

12. 2¾ *min* = [ ] secs

13. (19*ml* + [ ] ml) × 2 = 80*ml*

14. 16*g* + 14*g* = [ ] g

15. (45 + [ ]) ÷ 3 = 24

16. [ ] = 24 − 10 − 5

Marks [ ]

B INTO GEAR

1. Three times fifteen is how many? [ ]

2. Add together the odd numbers between 8 and 16. [ ]

3. How many will there be altogether in twenty groups of 4? [ ]

4. Divide seventy-two by four. [ ]

5. Seventeen plus 24 plus nine add eighteen is how many? [ ]

6. Write in the missing sign (+, −, × or ÷) in these sums:

4 × 15 = 30 [ ] 30   (46 − 17) [ ] 2 = 10 + 4½

Marks [ ]

C TOUGH CHALLENGE

1. If 6 items cost 90p. What is the cost of 4 items? [ ] p

2. Ian's pace measures ½ metre. How many of his paces measure 100 metres? [ ]

3. A packet of notepaper and a bottle of lemonade cost £1.50.

If the lemonade cost 80p how much did the notepaper cost? [ ] p

4. A money box contains £4.75. The coins are a mixture of TWENTIES, FIVES and TENS.

There are 15 TWENTIES and 9 TENS.

How many FIVES are there? [ ]

Marks [ ]

A START UP

1. $(9 \div 2) \times 3 =$ ⬚

2. $(14 \times 6) \div 4 = 63 \div$ ⬚

3. $- 9 + 23 = 47 -$ ⬚

4. $300 + 6000 + 20 =$ ⬚

5. ⬚ $= (46 \div 2) \times 4$

6. ⬚ km $\times 5 = 24km + 41km$

7. $2 + 3 =$ ⬚ *thirds*

8. $29 + 29 - 9 =$ ⬚

9. $27m - 15m = 72m \div$ ⬚

10. $5000 + 40 + 6 + 700 =$ ⬚

11. $1\frac{4}{10} =$ ⬚ *fifths*

12. $7\ min =$ ⬚ *seconds*

13. ⬚ $\div 70 = 12 - 5$

14. $4\ litres \times 25 =$ ⬚ litres

15. (⬚ $\div 3) + 34 = 55$

16. $39ml +$ ⬚ ml $= 87ml$

Marks ⬚

B INTO GEAR

1. Find the total of 38, twenty-seven and six. ⬚

2. Remove twenty-two from fifty and halve your answer. ⬚

3. Divide the sum of fifty-one and thirty-three by 3. ⬚

4. Forty-one minus fifteen add nine. ⬚

5. $100 + 200 + 300 + 400 + 500 + 600 + 700 + 800 + 900 + 1000 =$ ⬚

6. From 1000 subtract 150, 300, 50 and one hundred. ⬚

7. Which number is 8 times greater than ten? ⬚

Marks ⬚

C TOUGH CHALLENGE

1. In a cafe $\frac{1}{3}$ of the customers wore spectacles. There were 96 customers in the cafe.
   How many of them were not wearing spectacles? ⬚

2. Which 3 coins are given in change from £2.00 after spending £1.25? ⬚ p ⬚ p ⬚ p

3. How far will Susan travel in 20 minutes if she cycles ⬚ km
   at a constant speed of 15 kph?

4. The mass of 7 bags of screws is 700g. Each bag has the same mass.
   Work out the mass of three of the bags. ⬚ g

Marks ⬚

A START UP

1. ☐ − 1.4 − 2.6 = 0.6

2. 95 = (2 × ☐ × 2) + 3

3. ☐ , 129, 123, 117

4. ☐ m + 18m − 5m = 66m

5. ½ of 35 litres = ☐ litres

6. 0.7, 1.2, ☐ , 2.2, 2.7

7. 20 min × ☐ = 3 hours

8. 60 − 2 − 4 − 6 − 8 = ☐

9. 4ml × ☐ = 92ml

10. ¾ of 88 = ☐ − 16

11. 4km × ☐ = 80km

12. 297, 301, ☐ , 309, ☐

13. 48 − 9 + 4 − 5 = ☐ − 12

14. 39g − 15g + 34g = ☐ g

15. 19ml + ☐ ml = 63ml

16. 0.6 + 3.9 = ☐ quarters

Marks

B INTO GEAR

1. Thirty-seven add forty-six. ☐

2. What number is added to seventeen to make forty-four? ☐

3. Multiply 3 by seven and treble your answer. ☐

4. How many groups of four in one hundred? ☐

5. Work out the total of fifteen, twelve and twenty-five. ☐

6. By how many is 20 greater than six? ☐

7. Double nineteen and multiply your answer by two. ☐

Marks

C TOUGH CHALLENGE

1. Write as £s the sum of 29p, 24p and 36p. £ ☐

2. If 100 grams of blackcurrants cost 20p how much will 350 grams cost? ☐ p

3. Fencing posts at the edge of a field are 10 metres apart.

    Find in **metres** the distance between 9 of the posts. ☐ m

4. By how many **grams** is 760 grams less than 1 kilogram? ☐ g

5. Divide $\frac{1}{10}$ metre by five. How many **centimetres** is this? ☐ cm

6. Find the cost of one sticker if twenty cost £1. ☐ p

Marks

A START UP

1. ☐ , 79, 74, 69, 64, ☐

2. $14g + 28g - 22g =$ ☐ g

3. 2 months × ☐ = 2 years

4. $(£92 ÷ 4) × 2 =$ £ ☐

5. ☐ km = 17km + 26km

6. 15 days × 5 = ☐ days

7. 96, ☐ , 88, 84, ☐

8. 3¼ min = ☐ secs

9. $95p ÷ 5 =$ ☐ p

10. ☐ kg $- 17kg = 19kg$

11. (4km + ☐ km) × 6 = 54km

12. £80 × ☐ = £200 + £40

13. $27p + 15p + 8p =$ ☐ p

14. ☐ kg $- 28kg = 21kg$

15. 9cm × ☐ = 90cm ÷ 2

16. $^{6}/_{10}$ = 0.6 so $^{8}/_{10}$ = ☐

Marks ☐

B INTO GEAR

1. How many fours are worth seventy-six? ☐

2. What number is thirty-nine more than twenty-two? ☐

3. Find the difference between forty-eight and nineteen. ☐

4. Work out the product of five and sixteen. ☐

5. Divide seventy-two by three and halve the answer. ☐

6. What is the sum of 13, 15 and 16? ☐

7. Subtract 9 from twenty-three. Now minus eight from your answer. ☐

Marks ☐

C TOUGH CHALLENGE

1. How many minutes from 7.15am to 8.00am? ☐ min

2. Granny bought a box containing 250 straws. She uses 10 straws each week.

   How many weeks will the straws last? ☐ weeks

3. David had 3 TWENTIES, 5 TENS, 7 FIVES and 3 TWOS.

   How much had he altogether? £ ☐

4. How many bags of sweets each having a mass of 250 grams can be made

   from a ¾ kilogram pack? ☐ bags

Marks ☐

A START UP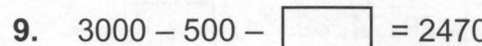

1. $37p + 16p + 55p =$ ☐ p

2. £ ☐ $- £39 = £52 - £14$

3. $(59km +$ ☐ km $) \times 8 = 800km$

4. $96\ months =$ ☐ years

5. ☐ $= ½\ of\ 83$

6. $\frac{3}{8}\ of\ 64 =$ ☐ $\times 6$

7. $(19 + 24 + 35) \div 2 =$ ☐

8. $(8 \times 12) + 54 =$ ☐ $+ 60$

9. $3000 - 500 -$ ☐ $= 2470$

10. $¾ + ½ + \frac{6}{8} =$ ☐

11. $5.25 - 1.75 - 0.75 =$ ☐

12. ☐ $\times 125cm = 7m\ 50cm$

13. $231cm \times$ ☐ $= 6m\ 93cm$

14. ☐ g $= 3kg\ 936g$

15. $3ml \times 2 \times 9 =$ ☐ ml

16. $0.9 + \frac{6}{10} + 0.4 =$ ☐ tenths

17. ☐ $= 1000 - (13 \times 7)$

18. $(9p \times 8) \div 4 = 59p -$ ☐ p

Marks ☐

B INTO GEAR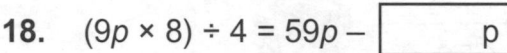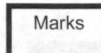

1. Round these numbers to the nearest thousand:

   34 620 ☐   93 255 ☐   71 002 ☐

2. Find the total of twenty-seven, 24 and sixty-three. ☐

3. What number is fifty-nine more than fifty-seven? ☐

4. Share eighty-four items equally among seven people. ☐

5. What is the product of six, three and four? ☐

6. 86 is how many more than 25? ☐

Marks ☐

C TOUGH CHALLENGE

1. Andrew decided to keep a diary. His first entry was on May 21st.

   His final entry was on July 19th.

   For how many days did he manage to keep his diary up-to-date? ☐ days

2. Ten metres of rope costs £15.00. Work out the cost of 14 metres. £ ☐

3. Write down the amount of flour that remains when 150g are removed

   from a 1kg bag. ☐ g

4. What fraction of 64 seconds is: 40secs? ☐   56secs? ☐

Marks ☐

A | START UP

1. $32p + 39p + 53p = \boxed{}$ p

2. $(\boxed{} \text{kg} - 58kg) \times 2 = 76kg$

3. $6cm \times \boxed{} = 96cm \div 2$

4. $\frac{4}{5} = 0.8$ so $\frac{3}{5} = \boxed{}$

5. $\boxed{}$ g $+ 58g = 156g$

6. $89 - \boxed{} - 16 - 13 = 30$

7. 381, 389, $\boxed{}$, 405, 413

8. $2m, 4m, \boxed{} m, 16m, 32m$

9. $(212 \times 4) \div \boxed{} = 424$

10. $\boxed{}$ km $\div 5 = 1.9km$

11. £9.25 + £8.75 + £3.50 = £ $\boxed{}$

12. $(99 \div 2) + \boxed{} = 55$

13. 1126, $\boxed{}$, 926, 826, 726

14. $(\boxed{} \text{ml} \times 5) \div 6 = 50ml$

15. $82g - \boxed{} g - 17g = 30g$

16. $\frac{3}{4} + \frac{2}{4} - \frac{5}{8} = \boxed{}$ eighths

17. $41m + 23m = 98m - \boxed{} m$

18. 9006, $\boxed{}$, 8992, 8985

Marks

B | INTO GEAR

1. What number is three times more than twenty-four? $\boxed{}$

2. How many is a nineth of 99? $\boxed{}$

3. Increase 33 by forty-five and then by fifty. $\boxed{}$

4. Decrease seven thousand by 1250. $\boxed{}$

5. Find the total of 65, 55 and four thousand five hundred. $\boxed{}$

6. Take twenty-four from eighty and find an $\frac{1}{8}$ of your answer. $\boxed{}$

7. Which number is 5 times greater than nineteen? $\boxed{}$

Marks

C | TOUGH CHALLENGE

1. If two angles of a triangle add up to 110° what is the size of the third angle? $\boxed{}$ °

2. Three children shared £6.00. Brett received ¼, Lynsey was given $\frac{1}{3}$ and James got $\frac{1}{6}$.

   How much money was left over? £ $\boxed{}$

3. Write as a decimal the difference between $\frac{3}{8}$ m and $\frac{5}{8}$ m. $\boxed{}$ m

4. Philip measured the diameter of a £1 coin and found it to be 22½mm.

   He placed 4 coins side by side in a straight line.

   Calculate the length of the line. $\boxed{}$ mm

Marks

1. $(96km \div 6) \times 3 = $ ☐ km

2. $(33 \times $ ☐ $) + 7 + 8 = 114$

3. ☐ kg $- 49kg = 29kg$

4. $3.45m + 5.55m = $ ☐ cm

5. $- 23 + $ ☐ $= 75$

6. $(79 - 12 - 42) \div 5 = $ ☐

7. $213cm \times $ ☐ $= 639cm$

8. $\frac{3}{5}$ of 70 *litres* = ☐ litres

9. $52p + 59p + 21p = $ ☐ p

10. $2.65m - 1.30m = $ ☐ m

11. $97 \div 2 = \frac{5}{10} + $ ☐

12. ☐ cm $= 2.5mm \times 4$

13. $(96 \div 8) + (62 - 26) = $ ☐

14. $3.65g + 2.2g + 3g = $ ☐ g

15. $3\frac{5}{7} = $ ☐ *sevenths*

16. $1\frac{1}{2} + \frac{3}{4} - \frac{3}{6} + 1\frac{5}{10} = $ ☐

17. ☐ $= (98 \div 7) \times 6$

18. ☐ km $+ 22km = 62km + 56km$

Marks ☐

B INTO GEAR

1. From ten thousand subtract 150. ☐

2. Give the number that is 1000 more than $65 + 68$. ☐

3. Write this number in figures: One thousand and nineteen. ☐

4. What is the remainder when 7 is shared into 59. ☐

5. A quarter of a hundred divided by two. ☐

6. Round these numbers to the nearest 1000:

23 768 ☐   90 003 ☐   45 063 ☐   76 780 ☐   Marks ☐

C TOUGH CHALLENGE

1. Abigail's aunty gave her £2.50 to make her money up to £11.25 so that she could buy the computer game she had always wanted.

How much had Abigail to start with? £ ☐

2. How much change from £8.00 after buying three books at £1.40 each? £ ☐

3. Write down the amount which is:

$\frac{1}{7}$ of 42 metres ☐ m $\frac{7}{8}$ of 88 seconds ☐ secs $\frac{3}{5}$ of 100 days ☐ days

4. Make 23 bottles of lemonade four times as many. ☐ bottles   Marks ☐

Exercise 17

A START UP

1. 4.65*m* + 3.45*m* = ____ m
2. ____ kg – 27*kg* = 73*kg*
3. – 44 + 83 + 13 + 34 = ____
4. *Find a fifth of* £8.50. £ ____
5. 65*km* ÷ ____ = 6½*km* × 5
6. ____ litres = 11 *litres* × 8
7. (37 + 19) ÷ ____ = 8
8. *Divide* 96 *by* 8. ____
9. ____ mm + 99*mm* = 196*mm*
10. 8 × (56 – 48) = ____
11. 96*ml* + ____ ml = 163*ml*
12. (____ + 43) ÷ 6 = 15
13. $1\frac{2}{5}$ + $\frac{8}{10}$ + 0.2 = ____ *fifths*
14. (10 × 4 × 8 × 2) ÷ 4 = ____
15. ____ = 76 – (100 ÷ 5)
16. *Subtract* 33*g from* 81*g*. ____ g
17. 4 + 5 + 2 = ____ *thirds*
18. (73 + 88 – 11) × 100 = ____

Marks

B INTO GEAR

1. Work out $\frac{2}{8}$ of ninety-six. ____
2. Write the following fractions as decimals:

   $\frac{1}{4}$ ____ $\frac{4}{5}$ ____ $\frac{6}{8}$ ____ $\frac{7}{10}$ ____
3. Twenty times three multiplied by seven is how many? ____
4. How many times less than sixty is 6? ____
5. Write down the number that is 14 times larger than 5. ____
6. Divide 50 by 2 and give your answer as a fraction of 100. ____

Marks

C TOUGH CHALLENGE

1. Which of these two lengths add up to 1km?

   429m 576m 571m 425m ____ m ____ m
2. How many grams less than 1kg 500g is the total of 40g, 520g, 210g & 130g? ____ g
3. Find the difference in cost between 5kg of dog food costing £1.40 per kg and 3kg of hamster litter costing £0.50 per kg. £ ____
4. A school textbook was 1.5cm thick.

   Write the height in centimetres of a pile of 50 of these books. ____ cm

Marks

A START UP

1. $6 \times 6\frac{2}{6}$ *litres* = ☐ litres

2. $99 - 26 - 24 + 80 =$ ☐

3. $\frac{2}{8}$ of 24 = (☐ ÷ 10) + 3

4. ½ of 77*km* = ☐ km

5. (☐ − 1.4 − 5.3) × 5 = 8.5

6. 65 = (3 × ☐ × 7) + 2

7. ☐ , 5003, 4997, 4991

8. ☐ *m* + 36*m* − 34*m* = 31*m*

9. £91.00 ÷ 2 = £☐

10. 36*g* ÷ 4 = 54*g* ÷ ☐

11. 156 *weeks* = ☐ *years*

12. $\frac{3}{8}$ of 16*cm* + 24*cm* = ☐ cm

13. (☐ × 4) + 202 = 302

14. ☐ km = ½ of 89*km*

15. 61 − ☐ − 13 − 14 = 22

16. 4 *sixths* = 2 ☐

17. 57.86*m* = ☐ *centimetres*

18. *Multiply 49½ by 2.* ☐

Marks ☐

B INTO GEAR

1. Divide ninety-six by four and your answer by six. ☐

2. Add together 76 and 77 and subtract your total from two hundred. ☐

3. Make nine hundred and ten 7 times as large. ☐

4. Increase 69 by fifty-one and share your answer by 3. ☐

5. Subtract the product of 2, 12 and 3 from three hundred. ☐

6. Round these numbers to the nearest 100:

   77 958 ☐   30 421 ☐   50 505 ☐   80 499 ☐   Marks ☐

C TOUGH CHALLENGE

1. The perimeter of a regular octagon is 48cm. Find the length of one side. ☐ cm

2. Give the single-digit number other than 1 and 2 which will divide exactly into:

   56, 28, 70 and 84. ☐

3. In a shop sale every item was reduced in price by 10%.

   John had spent £20.00 in the shop before the sale started.

   How much could he have saved on the same items if he had bought them

   during the sale? £ ☐   Marks ☐

A START UP

1. ½ of 67 mm = ☐ mm
2. − 30 + ☐ = 40 + 52 + 48
3. (31p + ☐ p) ÷ 7 = 10p
4. $^{20}/_8$ + 0.5 = ☐ halves
5. ☐ m − 28m = 24m + 45m
6. ☐ min × 12 = 84 min
7. (2.4 × 4) ÷ 3 = 2.1 + ☐
8. (84 ÷ 6) × (12 − 8) = ☐

9. 95 − 17 + 56 − 5 = ☐ − 11
10. 83g − 15g + 91g = ☐ g
11. 73ml + ☐ ml = 172ml
12. 0.5 + 2 + $^5/_{10}$ = ☐ tenths
13. Treble 29 = 160 − ☐
14. Total up 14, 28 and 46. ☐
15. ☐ ÷ 5 = 320
16. $^2/_7$ of 49 = 56 − ☐
17. 270m − 150m = 60m + ☐ m
18. 70 000 + 3 + 80 + 20 = ☐

Marks ☐

B INTO GEAR

1. Add 73 to 56 and subtract your answer from 250. ☐

2. Write in words the largest 4-digit number you can make from the figures 0, 7, 4 and 9.

☐

3. Decrease ninety by forty-seven and halve the answer. ☐

4. A fifth of fifteen hundred is how many? ☐

5. Divide $^2/_6$ of 72 by a third of twelve. ☐

Marks ☐

C TOUGH CHALLENGE

1. Which 3 of the following fractions when added together make a whole one?

$^2/_7$ $^4/_7$ $^3/_4$ $^1/_6$ $^2/_3$ $^1/_6$ $^2/_7$ ☐ ☐ ☐

2. Which two of these lengths can be divided by 6 without leaving a remainder?

84m, 56m, 78m, 33m, 99m ☐ m ☐ m

3. Find the average mass of the following three amounts and multiply the answer by treble 3: 45g, 28g and 26g. ☐ g

4. Leanne spent £1.88. List the 7 different coins she used to pay exactly for the items.

☐ ☐ ☐ ☐ ☐ ☐ ☐

Marks ☐

A START UP

1. 55 *litres* ÷ 2 = [litres]

2. [ml] − 53*ml* − 16*ml* = 25*ml*

3. 6.7*m* + 8.3*m* − 5.5*m* = [m]

4. *Multiply* 18.5 *by* 4. [ ]

5. ([ ] × 6) + 2 *min* = 80 *min*

6. 61*p* + [p] + 80*p* = £1.92

7. (⁷⁄₈ *of* 32) × (⅓ *of* 9) = [ ]

8. 74 − 35 = [ ] + 15 + 12

9. 72*cm* ÷ 8 = [cm]

10. 66*cm* + 74*cm* = [cm]

11. [ ] = (969 ÷ 3) × 2

12. (⁴⁄₈ *of* 96) + (⁵⁄₁₀ *of* 90) = [ ]

13. 7*ml* × [ ] = 42*ml*

14. ⁶⁄₇ *of* 49 = [ ] − 34

15. 250*m* × 2 × [ ] = 2*km*

16. 910, 830, [ ], 670, [ ]

17. *Change* ³⁰⁄₁₀ *to fifths.* [ ]

18. 8½ *min* = [ ] *seconds*

Marks [ ]

B INTO GEAR

1. Multiply treble forty-eight by nothing. [ ]

2. What number is seven times larger than eight? [ ]

3. How many fours have the same value as sixty-eight? [ ]

4. Subtract forty from 87 and double your answer. [ ]

5. 69 minus twenty-seven add fifty-eight. [ ]

6. How many do you add to each of these numbers to make 1000?

738 [ ]   412 [ ]   385 [ ]   653 [ ]   296 [ ]   90 [ ]

Marks [ ]

C TOUGH CHALLENGE

1. A cup has a mass of 220g. Work out ¾ of this mass. [g]

2. A woman jogged at an average speed of 8kph for 3¼ hours.

   What distance did she cover? [km]

3. John, Neil and Amy each had £10.00 to spend. John bought a book costing £6.50, Neil some computer disks costing £5.70 and Amy bought a bag. Between them they had £10.00 left. Use this information to work out the price of Amy's bag. [£]

4. A six-pack of pencils costs 42p. Find the cost of 4 pencils. [p]

Marks [ ]

A START UP

1. ½ of 87 *litres* = ☐ litres

2. 1.35, 1.41, ☐, 1.53, 1.59

3. 10 000 − ☐ = 5600

4. 88 − 8 − 5 − 9 − 7 = ☐

5. 9 × (64*g* − 57*g*) = ☐ g

6. ☐ km = 76*km* − 27*km* − 8*km*

7. ☐ = (35 ÷ 7) × (42 − 17)

8. 34*ml* + 48*ml* + 53*ml* = ☐ ml

9. 9 + 89 = (7 × ☐) + 0

10. 29½ = ½ of ☐

11. ☐, 12.26, 12.19, 12.12

12. 91*m* − 24*m* − 33*m* = ☐ m

13. − 18 + ☐ = 150 + 42

14. (☐ ÷ 4) × 6 = 90

15. 37.5*ml* + ☐ ml = 77*ml*

16. (6 × 13) + (52 + 54) = ☐

17. ☐ ÷ 50 = 30 − 17

18. 4 *litres* × 24 = ☐ litres

B INTO GEAR

Marks ☐

1. What is the product of five and eighteen? ☐

2. Find the total of seventy-six and sixty-eight. ☐

3. Round these numbers to the nearest 100:

   1648 ☐   9276 ☐   8149 ☐   6351 ☐

4. Decrease eighty by forty-six. ☐

5. How many sets of twenty in five hundred? ☐

6. Add fifty-five, twenty-nine and sixteen. ☐

Marks ☐

C TOUGH CHALLENGE

1. How many 750ml bottles can be filled from a container holding 3 litres? ☐ bottles

2. 4 boxes have a mass of 1 kilogram.

   What is the mass of 7 boxes in kilograms and grams? ☐ kg ☐ g

3. A square garden has a perimeter of 7.6m.

   Calculate the length of one side in metres and centimetres. ☐ m ☐ cm

4. After spending ⅘ of her money Linda had £1.50 left.

   How much had she at first? £ ☐

Marks ☐

21

A START UP

1. 10 × 8 = 16 × ⬚

2. ⬚ = (64 ÷ 8) × (28 ÷ 4)

3. 93p – ⬚p = 33p + 36p

4. ½ of 85m = ⬚ m ⬚ cm

5. 0.25, ½, 0.75, ⬚ , 1.25, 1½

6. 97g + 70g + 1kg = ⬚ g

7. 6745, ⬚ , 6731, 6724

8. (£65.00 ÷ 5) × 2 × 3 = £ ⬚

9. 77 ÷ ⬚ = 1011 – 1000

10. (842 ÷ 2) + 374 = ⬚

11. 1½ × 83kg = ½kg + ⬚ kg

12. 10 000 – 900 – 70 – 6 = ⬚

13. ⬚ ÷ 5 = 50% of 30

14. 8, 13, 21, ⬚ , 34, 39, 47, ⬚

15. 1.2m × 5 = ⬚ cm

16. 20mm × 4 = ⬚ cm × 2

17. (half of ⬚) × 3 = 2 × 48

18. 72ml + ⬚ ml = 150ml

Marks ⬚

B INTO GEAR

1. Add eighty to 23 + 47 and divide your answer by 3. ⬚

2. 24, 31, ⬚ , 45, 52, ⬚ , ⬚ , 73, ⬚ , 87, 94, ⬚

3. How many is 4/7 of 98? ⬚

4. 100 + 150 + 200 + 250 + 300 + 350 + 400 + 450 + 500 + 550 = ⬚

5. From 34½ multiplied by two subtract 42. ⬚

6. Total up all the single-digit numbers and subtract from 500. ⬚

7. From sixty take twenty-nine and seventeen. ⬚

8. Find the sum of the even numbers between 25 and 31. ⬚

Marks ⬚

C TOUGH CHALLENGE

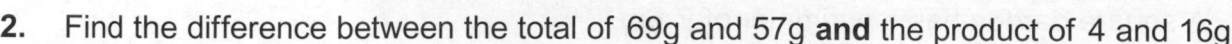

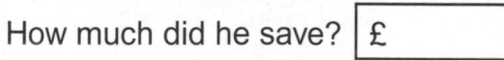

1. A clock is twenty minutes fast. The clock face shows the time as 6.15pm.

   Write the correct time in figures using the 24 hour clock. ⬚

2. Find the difference between the total of 69g and 57g **and** the product of 4 and 16g. ⬚ g

3. Of the money Carl received each week as pocket money

   he spent 60% and saved the rest. The amount he spent was £1.80.

   How much did he save? £ ⬚

Marks ⬚

A START UP

1. ³⁄₇ of 35 *litres* = [litres]

2. 2.9*g* + 2.6*g* = [g] − 1.7*g*

3. − 41 + 25 + 16 + 61 = [ ]

4. [ ] = 989 − 223 − 342 − 213

5. 74*ml* + 99*ml* = [ml]

6. *Multiply* 5 + 15 *by* 5. [ ]

7. 3.5 = [ ] *eighths*

8. *May + April* = [ ] *days*

9. [km] = 6*km* × 2 × 2 × 2 × 2

10. 32 *days* × 3 = [ ] *days*

11. *How many* 10s *in* 473? [ ]

12. 3⁴⁄₆ *min* = [ ] *seconds*

13. (62*ml* + [ml]) × 2 = 320*ml*

14. 36*g* + 47*g* + 67*g* = [g]

15. (45 *hrs* + [hrs]) ÷ 3 = 29 *hrs*

16. [ ] = 92 − 15 − 7 − 5 − 4 − 3

17. 81 ÷ 2 = [ ] + 20½

18. (½ of 92) − 20 − 16 = [ ]

Marks [ ]

B INTO GEAR

1. Divide sixty-four by four. [ ]

2. Write in the missing sign (+, −, ×, ÷) in these sums:

   48 [ ] 2 = 12 [ ] 12   99 [ ] 15 = 12 [ ] 7

3. How many will there be altogether in twenty groups of 5? [ ]

4. Twenty-six plus 35 plus six add fifty-three is how many? [ ]

5. What is half the product of six and twelve? [ ]

6. From 4000 subtract 250, 400, 50 and two hundred. [ ]

Marks [ ]

C TOUGH CHALLENGE

1. How many packets each containing 4 batteries can be filled from a stack of ninety-two batteries? [packets]

2. In a large carton there were 90 boxes of biscuits.

   How many boxes of biscuits would there be in 8 cartons? [boxes]

3. The mass of jam in a jar when full is 450g. The jar has a mass of 80 grams.

   Find the total mass of 3 full jars of jam in kilograms and grams. [kg   g]

4. Work out the sum of 1650cm and 5m 35cm in **m** and **cm**. [m   cm]

Marks [ ]

A START UP

1. ☐ = ½ of 77

2. $\frac{5}{8}$ of 64 = ☐ × 10

3. (17 + 35 + 26) ÷ 2 = ☐

4. (9 × 8) + 58 = ☐ + 50

5. 42*p* + 19*p* + 66*p* = ☐ p

6. (☐ kg − 45*kg*) × 2 = 96*kg*

7. 6*cm* × ☐ = 84*cm* ÷ 2

8. $\frac{2}{5}$ = 0.4 so $\frac{1}{5}$ = ☐

9. 2.55*g* + 3.4*g* + 4*g* = ☐ g

10. $4\frac{4}{9}$ = ☐ *ninths*

11. $2\frac{1}{2} + \frac{3}{4} - \frac{4}{8} + 3\frac{5}{10}$ = ☐

12. ☐ = (91 ÷ 7) × 5

13. ☐ km + 14*km* = 47*km* + 62*km*

14. ☐ mm + 78*mm* = 161*mm*

15. 8 × (68 − 64) = ☐

16. 99*ml* + ☐ ml = 142*ml*

17. (☐ + 47) ÷ 6 = 14

18. $2\frac{2}{5} + \frac{6}{10}$ + 0.8 = ☐ *fifths*

Marks ☐

B INTO GEAR

1. Divide 4000 by ten and multiply the answer by five. ☐

2. Work out the difference between 34 and 96. ☐

3. Add the odd numbers between 22 and 28. ☐

4. Find the total of sixty-one, twenty-three and fifty-three. ☐

5. Write in words the smallest 5-digit number you can make from the figures
   3, 7, 5, 9 and 1. ☐

6. Multiply an eighth of eighty by a half of ninety-eight. ☐

Marks ☐

C TOUGH CHALLENGE

1. There is 78p change from £2.00. How much has been spent? £ ☐

2. Which three coins together equal 45p? ☐ p ☐ p ☐ p

3. How many **hours** and **minutes** from midnight to quarter to five in the morning?

4. An aeroplane flew 2700km at a speed of 900km/h. ☐ hrs ☐ min
   How long did the journey take? ☐ hrs

5. Write 1800 grams to the nearest kilogram. ☐ kg

Marks ☐

A START UP

1. (☐ – 1.6 – 3.5) × 5 = 12.5

2. 75 = (3 × ☐ × 7) + 12

3. ☐ , 3997, 3991, 3985

4. ☐ m + 36m – 33m = 30m

5. ½ of 63mm = ☐ mm

6. – 20 + ☐ = 26 + 48 + 56

7. (34p + ☐ p) ÷ 7 = 12p

8. $^{24}/_{8}$ + 1.5 = ☐ halves

9. $^{5}/_{7}$ of 49 = ☐ – 46

10. 250m × 2 × ☐ = 3km

11. 810, 760, ☐ , 660, ☐

12. Change $^{40}/_{10}$ to fifths. ☐

13. 7¾ min = ☐ seconds

14. 8 + 52 = (5 × ☐) + 10

15. 49½ = ½ of ☐

16. ☐ , 13.33, 13.26, 13.19

17. 93m 25m – 36m = ☐ ııı

18. 96 ÷ ☐ = 48 ÷ 2

B INTO GEAR

Marks ☐

1. From twice seventy-eight subtract fifty-five. ☐

2. Add together the odd numbers between 18 and 24. ☐

3. Divide 90 by 6 and find $^{2}/_{5}$ of your answer. ☐

4. How many will there be altogether if there are seven groups of 14? ☐

5. Find the total of twenty-six, thirty-six and forty-six. ☐

6. By how many is thirty-seven less than 75? ☐

7. The result of making 26 treble the size will give how many? ☐

Marks ☐

C TOUGH CHALLENGE

1. Write 340cm to the nearest ½ metre. ☐ m

2. Write the total number of days in March, April and May. ☐ days

3. Mundeep has fifty-five pence and his brother has 4 times as much.

   How much have they altogether? £ ☐

4. Which 2 coins must be added to a TEN and 4 TWOS to make 25p? ☐ p ☐ p

5. What is the cost of 20cm of wood at £1.50 per metre? ☐ p

6. Find four-fifths of 1 kilogram. ☐ g

Marks ☐

A START UP

1. 1.25, 1½, 1.75, [   ], 2.25, 2½
2. 85g + 60g + 2kg = [   ] g
3. 5845, [   ], 5831, 5824
4. (£55.00 ÷ 5) × 2 × 4 = £ [   ]
5. ⁴⁄₇ of 35 litres = [   ] litres
6. 2.7g + 2.5g = [   ] g – 2g
7. – 43 + 24 + 18 + 57 = [   ]
8. [   ] = 999 – 234 – 433 – 111

9. [   ] g = 4kg 793g
10. 4ml × 2 × 6 = [   ] ml
11. 0.5 + ⁷⁄₁₀ + 0.9 = [   ] tenths
12. [   ] = 1000 – (15 × 5)
13. (7p × 8) ÷ 4 = 39p – [   ] p
14. (220 × 4) ÷ [   ] = 440
15. [   ] km ÷ 5 = 1.7km
16. £8.25 + £7.75 + £2.50 = £ [   ]
17. (88 ÷ 2) + [   ] = 51½
18. 2125, [   ], 1925, 1825

B INTO GEAR

Marks [   ]

1. What is the sum of seventeen, forty-seven and fifty-seven? [   ]
2. Decrease 95 by 19 and your answer by 25. [   ]
3. Find the product of three, four and five. [   ]
4. How many times can eight be subtracted from eighty-eight? [   ]
5. Make twenty-four plus nine greater by sixty-seven. [   ]
6. Subtract forty-eight from 96. [   ]
7. Divide one hundred by four and give your answer as a fraction of 100. [   ]

Marks [   ]

C TOUGH CHALLENGE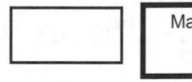

1. What is the difference in **millilitres** between 2 litres 600 millilitres
    and 3 litres 250 millilitres? [   ] ml
2. How many weeks will it take Josh to save £7.50 if he saves 25p a week? [   ] weeks
3. 1m of rope costs £3.60. Find the cost of 1½ m. £ [   ]
4. Work out the cost of 2½kg of carrots at 30p per kilogram. [   ] p
5. A jar of jam has a mass of 450g.

    Find to the nearest kilogram the mass of eight jars. [   ] kg

Marks [   ]

TEST 1 Time taken: .... min

Marks

1. 15 + 9 + 26 – 30 = ☐
2. (☐ ÷ 2) + 14 + 9 = 40
3. ☐ = (72 ÷ 4) × 5
4. 4.9 – 1.2 – 2.7 = 0.5 + ☐
5. (65 ÷ 5) + (41 – 15) = ☐
6. ¼ + ½ + ☐ + ½ = 2½
7. ☐ = 28 + 18 – 41 + 25
8. 3 × 3.3 = ☐ – 0.1
9. 14 + (5 × 3) = 43 – ☐
10. £4.20 ÷ ☐ = £0.70
11. (19 × ☐) + 5 + 4 = 85
12. 43 ÷ 2 = 1½ + ☐

TEST 2 Time taken: .... min

Marks

1. £300 × ☐ = £1850 – £50
2. 3 *sixths* = ☐ *quarters*
3. ☐ ÷ 2 = 17 + 25
4. 50 – 12 – 16 – 13 = ☐
5. 131, 128, ☐, 122, 119
6. (29 × 3) – ☐ = 77
7. ½ of 45 = 18 + ☐
8. ☐ × 44 = 4 × 22
9. (56 ÷ 2) × 3 = 2 × ☐
10. 4 × 3 × ☐ = 100 – 40
11. 1.9 + 1.2 + 1.4 + ☐ = 7
12. 0.5 = $\frac{5}{10}$ so ☐ = $\frac{9}{10}$

TEST 3 Time taken: .... min

Marks

1. 23½ = ½ of ☐
2. 87 ÷ 3 ÷ 2 = ☐
3. ☐ + 17 + 6 + 14 = 49
4. 6 × (50 – 15 – ☐) = 30
5. 309, ☐, 301, 297, 293
6. (4.7 – 2.8) × 2 = ☐ + 0.3
7. (☐ + 14 – 6) ÷ 3 = 11
8. (2 × 2 × 2 × 3) + ☐ = 47
9. 37 + 34 = ☐ + 29
10. (50 + ☐) ÷ 3 = 33
11. 889, 895, ☐, 907, ☐
12. ☐ × 20 = 10 × 8

TEST 4 Time taken: .... min

Marks

1. ¾ + 5 *quarters* + ½ = ☐
2. 0.6 = ☐ *fifths*
3. 12 + ☐ + 13 + 21 = 62
4. (92 ÷ 4) × 3 = ☐
5. ½ of ☐ = 10½
6. 1000 – 150 – ☐ = 600
7. (37 – 7 – 21) ÷ 3 = ☐
8. $\frac{1}{10}$ of 150 *equals*? ☐
9. *Total up* 26, 23 *and* 44. ☐
10. *Divide* 58 *by* 2. ☐
11. $\frac{3}{10}$ *of* 30 *equals*? ☐
12. *Multiply* 3 *by* 25. ☐

 TEST 5 — Time taken: .... min

Marks

1. ⅔ of 24 = ☐

2. 48, 53, ☐ , 63, 68, 73

3. 220 + 650 + 110 = ☐

4. ½ of 66 = ☐ + 15

5. 28 + ☐ − 12 = 32

6. ½ + ¼ + ¾ + ⁵⁄₁₀ = ☐

7. (5 × 4 × 5) ÷ 10 = ☐

8. 47 − ☐ = 72 ÷ 2

9. 1.5 − 0.3 − 0.7 = ☐

10. 29 + 29 − 9 = ☐ + 25

11. ☐ = 45 − 6 − 7 − 5

12. (65 ÷ 5) + 7 = 47 − ☐

 TEST 6 — Time taken: .... min

Marks

1. 5 × 90 = 50 + 175 + ☐

2. (9 + 3) × ☐ = 38 + 34

3. (☐ − 13) = (14 × 3) − 28

4. 0.8 ÷ ☐ = 1.6 ÷ 4

5. (21 + 19) × 2 = ½ of ☐

6. ☐ + 11 = 32 − 13

7. (41 − 10 − 16) = 90 ÷ ☐

8. 42 + ☐ + 42 = 100

9. ☐ + 16 = 33 × 2

10. 2.4 + 0.7 = 4.5 − ☐

11. 24 − ☐ − 5 = 36 ÷ 4

12. ☐ + 17 + 5 + 14 = 48

 TEST 7 — Time taken: .... min

Marks

1. 37 = 18 + ☐

2. 54 ÷ ☐ = 33 − 15

3. ⁷⁄₁₀ + ⅖ = ☐ tenths

4. 6 × 7 = ☐ × 3

5. (13 + 31 + 4) ÷ 4 = ☐

6. ☐ − 29 = 3 + 5 + 7 + 4

7. 68 ÷ ☐ = 85 ÷ 5

8. 36 − 19 + 42 = ☐

9. ☐ = ½ of 23

10. (½ of 70) − 15 = ☐

11. ☐ + 14 = 6 × 9

12. ☐ + 2.1 = 4.9 − 1.9

TEST 8 — Time taken: .... min

Marks

1. 48 = 17 + 13 + 5 + ☐

2. 13 = 52 ÷ ☐

3. ☐ thirds = 4 sixths

4. (9 ÷ 2) × 3 = 10 + ☐

5. 5 × (33 − 16) = ☐

6. 42 − 7 − 8 − 9 − ☐ = 10

7. ☐ , 94, 89, 84, 79, 74

8. ☐ × 3 = (50 ÷ 2) + 14

9. 38 − 29 = 1½ × ☐

10. (14 × 3) ÷ 2 = ½ of ☐

11. 92, 88, 84, ☐ , 76, 72

12. ⁴⁄₂ + ⁸⁄₄ + ²⁰⁄₁₀ + ⁶⁄₃ = ☐

28

 **TEST 9**   Time taken: .... min

Marks

1. 25 × 4 = ☐

2. ☐ = 80 ÷ 4 ÷ 2 ÷ 5

3. ³⁄₁₀ of 80 = ☐

4. 90 ÷ 5 = ☐ – 16

5. ⅙ of 78 + ⅓ of 9 = ☐

6. ☐ = 44 – 12 – 26

7. (☐ ÷ 3) × 2 = 34

8. 41 – 27 = ☐ + 3 + 7

9. 48 + 34 = ☐ × 41

10. 38 – ☐ = (6 × 12) ÷ 3

11. ☐ = 2 × 1.9

12. ½ of 31 = ☐

 **TEST 10**   Time taken: .... min

Marks

1. (☐ ÷ 5) × 4 = 60

2. 48 ÷ ☐ = 8 × 3

3. 80 + 800 + 8 = ☐

4. 46 – 7 + 3 = ☐ – 3

5. 1.4 + 0.9 + 2.8 = ☐

6. 32 + ☐ = 3 + 40 + 27

7. (10 × 5) + ☐ = 16 × 5

8. ☐ ÷ 6 = 2 × 7

9. 4 × 9 = 3 × ☐

10. ☐ + 16 – 6 = 58

11. 45 – 6 – 17 = ☐ – 25

12. ☐ = ½ of 39

TEST 11   Time taken: .... min

Marks

1. ½ of 25 = ☐

2. 24 + ☐ = 34 + 23

3. 191, 197, 203, ☐

4. (45 + ☐) ÷ 3 = 24

5. ☐ × 6 = 46 + 16 + 16

6. 4½ × ☐ = 27 ÷ 3

7. 5.5 = ☐ quarters

8. 38 – 19 = 8 + ☐

9. ¾ of 44 = 50 – ☐

10. (72 ÷ 4) × 5 = ☐ × 9

11. ☐ × 9 = 40 – 20 + 25

12. ⁵⁄₁₀ = 0.5 so ⁸⁄₁₀ = ☐

TEST 12   Time taken: .... min

Marks

1. ☐ – 21 = 26

2. 18 + ☐ + 16 = 47

3. ☐ = (76 ÷ 4) × 3

4. 17 + ☐ + 4 = 65

5. 38 + 21 – 5 + 3 = ☐

6. (☐ ÷ 4) + 1 = 33 – 25

7. 3 × ☐ = 15 + 1½

8. 65 = (2 × ☐ × 2) + 1

9. ☐ – 21 = 9 + 9

10. (31 + 17) ÷ 3 = ☐

11. ½ of 19 = ☐ of 38

12. 6 × (31 – 18) = ☐

TEST 13  Time taken: .... min

Marks

1. $\frac{1}{5} = 0.2$ so $\frac{2}{5} = $ [ ]

2. $(8 \times 12) + 54 = $ [ ] $ + 60$

3. [ ] $ + 58 = 100 + 6 + 50$

4. $4\frac{3}{7} = $ [ ] *sevenths*

5. $381, 389,$ [ ] $, 405, 413$

6. $55 + 16 + 37 = $ [ ]

7. $(423 \times 2) - $ [ ] $ = 756$

8. $\frac{4}{8} + \frac{2}{4} - \frac{5}{8} = $ [ ] *eighths*

9. $(95 \div 2) + $ [ ] $ = 50$

10. $\frac{5}{8}$ of $64 = $ [ ] $ \times 2$

11. $£3.50 + £8.75 + £9.25 = $ £[ ]

12. $82 - $ [ ] $ - 17 = 90 \div 3$

TEST 14  Time taken: .... min

Marks

1. [ ] $ = 1000 - (13 \times 7)$

2. $1126,$ [ ] $, 926, 826, 726$

3. [ ] $ - 26 = 91 - 63$

4. $(91 \div 7) \times 5 = $ [ ] $ - 9$

5. [ ] $ + 98 = 186$

6. $312 \times $ [ ] $ = 936$

7. $\frac{3}{4} + \frac{1}{2} + \frac{6}{8} + \frac{3}{4} = $ [ ]

8. $\frac{4}{5}$ of $70 = $ [ ]

9. [ ] $ + 22 = 25 + 37 + 56$

10. $9 \times 2 \times 3 = $ [ ]

11. $1\frac{1}{2} + 1\frac{3}{4} - \frac{3}{6} + 1\frac{5}{10} = $ [ ]

12. [ ] $ - 49 = 29$

TEST 15  Time taken: .... min

Marks

1. $41 + 23 = 98 - $ [ ]

2. $(59 + $ [ ] $) \times 8 = 800$

3. $89 - $ [ ] $ - 16 - 13 = 30$

4. [ ] $ \times 125 = 750$

5. $3, 6, 12,$ [ ] $, 48, 96$

6. $32 + 39 + 53 = $ [ ]

7. [ ] $ = \frac{1}{2}$ of 93

8. $(9 \times 8) \div 4 = 59 - $ [ ]

9. $9005,$ [ ] $, 8991, 8984$

10. $(19 + 24 + 35) \div 2 = $ [ ]

11. $($ [ ] $ - 58) \times 2 = 76$

12. $($ [ ] $ \times 5) \div 6 = 75 - 25$

TEST 16  Time taken: .... min

Marks

1. $0.7 + \frac{3}{10} + 0.8 = $ [ ] *tenths*

2. [ ] $ \div 7 = 0.9$

3. $6.45 + 2.55 = $ [ ]

4. $6 \times $ [ ] $ = 96 \div 2$

5. $(79 - 32 - 12) \div 7 = $ [ ]

6. $231 \times $ [ ] $ = 693$

7. 108 *months* $ = $ [ ] *years*

8. $(52 + 59 + 21) \times 2 = $ [ ]

9. [ ] $ = (98 \div 7) \times 6$

10. $(33 \times $ [ ] $) + 7 + 8 = 114$

11. $5.25 - 1.75 - 0.75 = $ [ ]

12. $7000 - 400 - $ [ ] $ = 6530$

 **TEST 17**   Time taken: .... min

Marks

1. £91.00 ÷ 2 = £ ⬚

2. 1²⁄₅ + ⁸⁄₁₀ + 0.2 = ⬚ *fifths*

3. (10 × 4 × 8 × 2) ÷ 4 = ⬚

4. *Find a fifth of £8.50* £ ⬚

5. ½ of 67 = ⬚ + 3.5

6. (31 + ⬚) ÷ 7 = 10

7. 4.65 + 3.45 = ⬚ − 1.9

8. 96 + ⬚ = 163

9. 83 − 15 + 91 = ⬚

10. ⬚ + 99 = 98 + 98

11. 0.5 + 3 + ⁵⁄₁₀ = ⬚ *tenths*

12. ⬚ − 28 = 24 + 45

 **TEST 18**   Time taken: .... min

Marks

1. 95 − 17 + 56 − 5 = ⬚ − 11

2. 270 − 150 = 60 + ⬚

3. ⬚ − 27 = 50 + 23

4. (84 ÷ 6) × (12 − 8) = ⬚

5. 40 000 + 2 + 70 + 10 = ⬚

6. ⬚ ÷ 5 = 420

7. 64 + 83 + 13 + 34 = ⬚

8. ²⁄₈ of 24 = (⬚ ÷ 10) + 3

9. 4 + 5 + 2 = ⬚ *sevenths*

10. 65 = (3 × ⬚ × 7) + 2

11. ⬚ , 4003, 3997, 3991

12. ⬚ + 36 − 34 = 31

 **TEST 19**   Time taken: .... min

Marks

1. ²⁄₇ of 49 = 56 − ⬚

2. 65 ÷ ⬚ = 6½ × 5

3. ⬚ = 76 − (100 ÷ 5)

4. 74 + ⬚ = 40 + 52 + 48

5. *Divide 96 by 8.* ⬚

6. 8 × (56 − 48) = ⬚ + 32

7. ²⁰⁄₈ + 2.5 = ⬚ *halves*

8. (37 + 19) ÷ ⬚ = 8

9. (⬚ + 43) ÷ 6 = 15

10. 73 + ⬚ = 90 + 80 + 2

11. *Treble 29 = 160 −* ⬚

12. *Total up 28, 14 and 46.* ⬚

 **TEST 20**   Time taken: .... min

Marks

1. *Divide 88 by 8.* ⬚

2. (73 + 88 − 11) × 100 = ⬚

3. (2.4 × 4) ÷ 3 = 2.4 + ⬚

4. *Subtract 29 from 85.* ⬚

5. ⬚ × 12 = 12 × 7

6. 8 × 8²⁄₈ = ⬚

7. 99 − 26 − 24 + 80 = ⬚

8. ½ of 77 = ⬚

9. (⬚ − 1.4 − 5.3) × 5 = 8.5

10. *Multiply 49½ by 2.* ⬚

11. 38.49m = ⬚ *centimetres*

12. 4 *eighths* = 1 ⬚

 **TEST 21** | Time taken: .... min

Marks

1. 72 ÷ 8 = ☐

2. 8, 13, 21, ☐ , 34, 39, 47, ☐

3. 6745, ☐ , 6731, 6724

4. 93 − ☐ = 33 + 36

5. 0.25, ½, 0.75, ☐ , 1.25, 1½

6. (842 ÷ 2) + 374 = ☐

7. 99 + ☐ = 150 + 42

8. (65 ÷ 5) × 2 × 3 = ☐

9. ☐ , 12.26, 12.19, 12.12

10. ☐ ÷ 50 = 30 − 17

11. 10 000 − ☐ = 5600

12. (6 × 13) + (52 + 54) = ☐

 **TEST 22** | Time taken: .... min

Marks

1. ☐ = (35 ÷ 7) × (42 − 17)

2. (☐ ÷ 4) × 6 = 90

3. 6.7 + 8.3 − 5.5 = ☐

4. 9 + 89 = (7 × ☐) + 0

5. 74 − 35 = ☐ + 15 + 12

6. 88 − 8 − 5 − 9 − 7 = ☐

7. *Multiply* 18.5 *by* 4. ☐

8. $^6/_7$ of 49 = ☐ − 34

9. 1.35, 1.41, ☐ , 1.53

10. (*half of* ☐) × 3 = 2 × 48

11. *Change* $^{30}/_{10}$ *to fifths.* ☐

12. 7 × ☐ = 42

 **TEST 23** | Time taken: .... min

Marks

1. 9 × (64 − 57) = ☐

2. ☐ ÷ 5 = 50% of 30

3. 81 ÷ 2 = ☐ + 20½

4. 10 000 − 900 − 70 − 6 = ☐

5. ☐ = (64 ÷ 8) × (28 ÷ 4)

6. 1½ × 83 = ½ + ☐

7. 77 ÷ ☐ = 1011 − 1000

8. 91 − 24 − 33 = ☐

9. 29½ = ½ of ☐

10. *How many* 10s *in* 849? ☐

11. 37.5 + ☐ = 82

12. 34 + 48 + 53 = ☐

 **TEST 24** | Time taken: .... min

Marks

1. ☐ = (969 ÷ 3) × 2

2. ☐ − 53 − 16 = 25

3. ($^7/_8$ *of* 32) × ($^1/_3$ *of* 9) = ☐

4. 250 × 2 × ☐ = 10 000

5. ☐ = 76 − 27 − 8

6. 66 + 74 = ☐

7. 910, 830, ☐ , 670, ☐

8. ½ of 87 = ☐

9. (☐ × 6) + 2 = 80

10. ($^4/_8$ *of* 96) + ($^5/_{10}$ *of* 90) = ☐

11. (½ *of* 92) − 20 − 16 = ☐

12. 61 + ☐ + 80 = 192

Answers — Pages 1 to 11

Page 1 Ex 1
A – START UP
1. 13p 2. 27kg 3. 9km 4. 5
5. 11½ 6. 54 litres 7. 12 8. 6
9. 32 10. 1½ 11. 05 12. 5 13. 2
14. 68m 15. 13 hrs 16. 3 tenths
B – INTO GEAR
1. 55 2. 60 3. 70 4. 17
5. 2800, 3600, 5100 6. 3
C – TOUGH CHALLENGE
1. 20p, 20p, 5p, 2p 2. 3 hrs
3. 50p, 20p, 5p 4. 66 drinks
5. one thousand five hundred

Page 2 Ex 2
A – START UP
1. 50p 2. 48kg 3. 3 4. 0.7 5. 38g
6. 12 7. 1700 8. 1130 9. 2
10. 0.8km 11. £10.70 12. 10
13. 53 14. 14ml 15. 25g 16. 2¼
B – INTO GEAR
1. 41 2. 18 3. 95 4. 20 5. 60
6. 4550 7. 1420
C – TOUGH CHALLENGE
1. 4cm 2. 63g 3. 85p 4. 16p

Page 3 Ex 3
A – START UP
1. 90km 2. 4 3. 38kg 4. 600cm
5. 18g 6. 3 7. 6 8. 14 litres
9. 92p 10. 1.1m 11. 20 12. 80mm
13. 31 14. 7.3 15. 22 hrs 16. 1
B – INTO GEAR
1. 24 2. 3000, 6000, 9000, 5000
3. 45 4. 270 5. 4 6. 379
C – TOUGH CHALLENGE
1. 47 2. 61 3. 31
4. 50p, 20p, 5p 5. 48

Page 4 Ex 4
A – START UP
1. 3.75m 2. 38kg 3. 40 4. £7.50
5. 3 6. 64 litres 7. 5 8. 27
9. 18mm 10. 85 11. 22ml
12. 31 13. 9 quarters 14. 16
15. 26 16. 24g
B – INTO GEAR
1. 53 2. 10 3. 4 4. 88 5. 90
6. 12 7. 36
C – TOUGH CHALLENGE
1. 62 cups 2. 1.00pm 3. 20km
4. 65p 5. Sue, 1

Page 5 Ex 5
A – START UP
1. 21 litres 2. 45 3. 6 4. 12½km
5. 4.5 6. 16 7. 185 8. 48m 9. £5.50
10. 24cm 11. 22 hrs 12. 11 13. 5
14. 16½ 15. 17 16. tenths
B – INTO GEAR
1. 72 2. 840 3. 5 4. 3000, 6000,
9000, 8000 5. 12 6. 77
C – TOUGH CHALLENGE
1. £2.40 2. 40g 3. 70cm 4. 80

Page 6 Ex 6
A – START UP
1. 15½ 2. 77 3. 27p 4. 7 halves
5. 39m 6. 5 min 7. 1.1 8. 68
9. 37 10. 58g 11. 44ml
12. 10 quarters 13. 76 14. 57
15. 75 16. 17
B – INTO GEAR
1. 16 2. one hundred and seventy-nine
3. nine hundred and seventy-five
4. 16 5. 9
C – TOUGH CHALLENGE
1. 42cm 2. 92 days 3. $^6/_{10}$, ($^3/_5$), ¾
4. 77p 5. 3m

Page 7 Ex 7
A – START UP
1. 13½ litres 2. 47ml 3. 5.1 4. 81
5. 13 min 6. 44p 7. 120 8. 4
9. 18cm 10. 65cm 11. 4 12. 16
13. 31 14. 49 15. 20 16. 135, 143
B – INTO GEAR
1. 55 2. 27 3. 48
4. 27, 59, 62, 35, 71, 86 5. 0 6. 10
C – TOUGH CHALLENGE
1. 15 pins 2. 60 months 3. 10
4. 225cm 5. 36 6. 40p

Page 8 Ex 8
A – START UP
1. 19½ litres 2. 1.6 3. 12 4. 26
5. 85 6. 8km 7. 57 8. 82ml 9. 5
10. 49 11. 899 12. 22m 13. 62
14. 51 15. 40ml 16. 78
B – INTO GEAR
1. 15 2. 42 3. 50 4. 88 5. 170,
430, 810, 630, 370 6. 13
C – TOUGH CHALLENGE
1. 75p 2. 52cm 3. £7.00 4. 4 bars
5. £0.39 6. 36p

Page 9 Ex 9
A – START UP
1. 6 2. 30 3. 13 4. 15m
5. 74, 49 6. 32g 7. 12 8. £26
9. 3 10. 19 hrs 11. 18½kg
12. 2270 13. 84 14. 406, 386
15. 380cm 16. 12
B – INTO GEAR
1. 96 2. 55 3. 8 4. 15
5. 62, 44, 38, 26, 8 6. 57 7. 84
C – TOUGH CHALLENGE
1. £25.00, £16.00 2. 5p, 2p
3. 55g 4. 540 miles

Page 10 Ex 10
A – START UP
1. 16 litres 2. 4.9 3. 26 4. 27
5. 33ml 6. 16 7. 3 thirds
8. 29 hrs 9. 37km 10. 65 days
11. 88, 76 12. 165secs 13. 21ml
14. 30g 15. 27 16. 9
B – INTO GEAR
1. 45 2. 48 3. 80 4. 18
5. 68 6. +, ÷
C – TOUGH CHALLENGE
1. 60p 2. 200 3. 70p 4. 17

Page 11 Ex 11
A – START UP
1. 13½ 2. 3 3. 33 4. 6320 5. 92
6. 13km 7. 15 thirds 8. 49 9. 6
10. 5746 11. 7 fifths 12. 420
seconds 13. 490 14. 100 litres
15. 63 16. 48ml
B – INTO GEAR
1. 71 2. 14 3. 28 4. 35 5. 5500
6. 400 7. 80
C – TOUGH CHALLENGE
1. 64 2. 5p, 20p, 50p 3. 5km
4. 300g

Answers — Pages 12 to 22

Page 12 Ex 12
A – START UP
1. 4.6 **2.** 23 **3.** 135 **4.** 53m
5. 17½ litres **6.** 1.7 **7.** 9 **8.** 40
9. 23 **10.** 82 **11.** 20 **12.** 305, 313
13. 50 **14.** 58g **15.** 44ml
16. 18 quarters
B – INTO GEAR
1. 83 **2.** 27 **3.** 63 **4.** 25 **5.** 52
6. 14 **7.** 76
C – TOUGH CHALLENGE
1. £0.89 **2.** 70p **3.** 80m **4.** 240g
5. 2cm **6.** 5p

Page 13 Ex 13
A – START UP
1. 84, 59 **2.** 20g **3.** 12 **4.** £46
5. 43km **6.** 75 days **7.** 92, 80
8. 195 secs **9.** 19p **10.** 36kg
11. 5km **12.** 3 **13.** 50p **14.** 49kg
15. 5 **16.** 0.8
B – INTO GEAR
1. 19 **2.** 61 **3.** 29 **4.** 80 **5.** 12
6. 44 **7.** 6
C – TOUGH CHALLENGE
1. 45 min **2.** 25 weeks **3.** £1.51
4. 3 bags

Page 14 Ex 14
A – START UP
1. 108p **2.** £77 **3.** 41km **4.** 8 years
5. 41½ **6.** 4 **7.** 39 **8.** 90 **9.** 30
10. 2 **11.** 2.75 **12.** 6 **13.** 3
14. 3936g **15.** 54ml **16.** 19 tenths
17. 909 **18.** 41p
B – INTO GEAR
1. 35 000, 93 000, 71 000 **2.** 114
3. 116 **4.** 12 **5.** 72 **6.** 61
C – TOUGH CHALLENGE
1. 60 days **2.** £21.00 **3.** 850g
4. ⅝, ⅞

Page 15 Ex 15
A – START UP
1. 124p **2.** 96kg **3.** 8 **4.** 0.6
5. 98g **6.** 30 **7.** 397 **8.** 8m **9.** 2
10. 9.5km **11.** £21.50 **12.** 5½
13. 1026 **14.** 60ml **15.** 35g
16. 5 eighths **17.** 34m **18.** 8999
B – INTO GEAR
1. 72 **2.** 11 **3.** 128 **4.** 5750
5. 4620 **6.** 7 **7.** 95
C – TOUGH CHALLENGE
1. 70° **2.** £1.50 **3.** 0.25m **4.** 90mm

Page 16 Ex 16
A – START UP
1. 48km **2.** 3 **3.** 78kg **4.** 9cm
5. 98 **6.** 5 **7.** 3 **8.** 42 litres
9. 132p **10.** 1.35m **11.** 48 **12.** 1cm
13. 48 **14.** 8.85g **15.** 26 sevenths
16. 3¼ **17.** 84 **18.** 96km
B – INTO GEAR
1. 9850 **2.** 1133 **3.** 1019
4. 3 **5.** 12½
6. 24 000, 90 000, 45 000, 77 000
C – TOUGH CHALLENGE
1. £8.75 **2.** £3.80
3. 6m, 77 secs, 60 days **4.** 92 bottles

Page 17 Ex 17
A – START UP
1. 8.10m **2.** 100kg **3.** 86 **4.** £1.70
5. 2 **6.** 88 litres **7.** 7 **8.** 12
9. 97mm **10.** 64 **11.** 67ml **12.** 47
13. 12 fifths **14.** 160 **15.** 56
16. 48g **17.** 33 thirds **18.** 15 000
B – INTO GEAR
1. 24 **2.** 0.25, 0.80, 0.75, 0.70
3. 420 **4.** 10 **5.** 70 **6.** ¼
C – TOUGH CHALLENGE
1. 429m, 571m **2.** 600g **3.** £5.50
4. 75cm

Page 18 Ex 18
A – START UP
1. 38 litres **2.** 129 **3.** 30 **4.** 38½km
5. 8.4 **6.** 3 **7.** 5009 **8.** 29m
9. £45.50 **10.** 6 **11.** 3 years
12. 30cm **13.** 25 **14.** 44½km
15. 12 **16.** thirds
17. 5786 centimetres **18.** 99
B – INTO GEAR
1. 4 **2.** 47 **3.** 6370 **4.** 40 **5.** 228
6. 78 000, 30 400, 50 500, 80 500
C – TOUGH CHALLENGE
1. 6cm **2.** 7 **3.** £2.00

Page 19 Ex 19
A – START UP
1. 33½mm **2.** 170 **3.** 39p
4. 6 halves **5.** 97m **6.** 7 min
7. 1.1 **8.** 56 **9.** 140 **10.** 159g
11. 99ml **12.** 30 tenths **13.** 73
14. 88 **15.** 1600 **16.** 42 **17.** 60m
18. 70 103
B – INTO GEAR
1. 121 **2.** nine thousand, seven
hundred and forty
3. 21½ **4.** 300 **5.** 6
C – TOUGH CHALLENGE
1. ⅙, ⅙, ⅔ **2.** 84m, 78m **3.** 297g
4. £1, 50p, 20p, 10p, 5p, 2p, 1p

Page 20 Ex 20
A – START UP
1. 27½ litres **2.** 94ml **3.** 9.5m
4. 74 **5.** 13 **6.** 51p **7.** 84 **8.** 12
9. 9cm **10.** 140cm **11.** 646 **12.** 93
13. 6 **14.** 76 **15.** 4 **16.** 750, 590
17. ¹⁵⁄₅ **18.** 510 seconds
B – INTO GEAR
1. 0 **2.** 56 **3.** 17 **4.** 94 **5.** 100
6. 262, 588, 615, 347, 704, 910
C – TOUGH CHALLENGE
1. 165g **2.** 26km **3.** £7.80 **4.** 28p

Page 21 Ex 21
A – START UP
1. 43½ litres **2.** 1.47 **3.** 4400 **4.** 59
5. 63g **6.** 41km **7.** 125 **8.** 135ml
9. 14 **10.** 59 **11.** 12.33 **12.** 34m
13. 210 **14.** 60 **15.** 39.5ml
16. 184 **17.** 650 **18.** 96 litres
B – INTO GEAR
1. 90 **2.** 144 **3.** 1600, 9300, 8100, 6400
4. 34 **5.** 25 **6.** 100
C – TOUGH CHALLENGE
1. 4 bottles **2.** 1kg 750g **3.** 1m 90cm
4. £7.50

Page 22 Ex 22
A – START UP
1. 5 **2.** 56 **3.** 24p **4.** 42m 50cm
5. 1 **6.** 1167g **7.** 6738 **8.** £78.00
9. 7 **10.** 795 **11.** 124kg **12.** 9024
13. 75 **14.** 26, 52 **15.** 600cm
16. 4cm **17.** 64 **18.** 78ml
B – INTO GEAR
1. 50 **2.** 38, 59, 66, 80, 101 **3.** 56
4. 3250 **5.** 27 **6.** 455 **7.** 14 **8.** 84
C – TOUGH CHALLENGE
1. 17:55 **2.** 62g **3.** £1.20

Answers — Pages 23 to 32

Page 23 Ex 23
A – START UP
1. 15 litres   2. 7.2g   3. 61   4. 211
5. 173ml   6. 100   7. 28 eighths
8. 61 days   9. 96km   10. 96 days
11. 47   12. 220 seconds   13. 98ml
14. 150g   15. 42 hrs   16. 58
17. 20   18. 10
B – INTO GEAR
1. 16   2. ÷, +, −, ×   3. 100   4. 120
5. 36   6. 3100
C – TOUGH CHALLENGE
1. 23 packets   2. 720 boxes
3. 1kg 590g   4. 21m 85cm

Page 24 Ex 24
A – START UP
1. 38½   2. 4   3. 39   4. 80   5. 127p
6. 93kg   7. 7   8. 0.2   9. 9.95g
10. 40 ninths   11. 6¼   12. 65
13. 95km   14. 83mm   15. 32
16. 43ml   17. 37   18. 19 fifths
B – INTO GEAR
1. 2000   2. 62   3. 75   4. 137
5. thirteen thousand, five hundred and
   seventy-nine   6. 490
C – TOUGH CHALLENGE
1. £1.22   2. 20p, 20p, 5p
3. 4 hrs 45 min   4. 3 hrs   5. 2kg

Page 25 Ex 25
A – START UP
1. 7.6   2. 3   3. 4003   4. 27m
5. 31½mm   6. 150   7. 50p
8. 9 halves   9. 81   10. 6
11. 710, 610   12. ²⁰⁄₅
13. 465 seconds   14. 10   15. 99
16. 13.40   17. 32m   18. 4
B – INTO GEAR
1. 101   2. 63   3. 6   4. 98   5. 108
6. 38   7. 78
C – TOUGH CHALLENGE
1. 3½ m   2. 92 days   3. £2.75
4. 2p, 5p   5. 30p   6. 800g

Page 26 Ex 26
A – START UP
1. 2   2. 2145g   3. 5838   4. £88.00
5. 20 litres   6. 7.2g   7. 56   8. 221
9. 4793g   10. 48ml   11. 21 tenths
12. 925   13. 25p   14. 2   15. 8.5km
16. £18.50   17. 7½   18. 2025
B – INTO GEAR
1. 121   2. 51   3. 60   4. 11
5. 100   6. 48   7. ¼
C – TOUGH CHALLENGE
1. 650ml   2. 30 weeks   3. £5.40
4. 75p   5. 4kg

Page 27 Time Yourself Tests
Test 1
1. 20   2. 34   3. 90   4. 0.5   5. 39
6. 1¼   7. 30   8. 10   9. 14   10. 6
11. 4   12. 20
Test 2
1. 6   2. 2 quarters   3. 84   4. 9
5. 125   6. 10   7. 4½   8. 2   9. 42
10. 5   11. 2.5   12. 0.9
Test 3
1. 47   2. 14½   3. 12   4. 30   5. 305
6. 3.5   7. 25   8. 23   9. 42   10. 49
11. 901, 913   12. 4
Test 4
1. 2½   2. 3 fifths   3. 16   4. 69
5. 21   6. 250   7. 3   8. 15   9. 93
10. 29   11. 9   12. 75

Page 28 Time Yourself Tests
Test 5
1. 16   2. 58   3. 980   4. 18   5. 16
6. 2¼   7. 10   8. 11   9. 0.5   10. 24
11. 27   12. 27
Test 6
1. 225   2. 6   3. 27   4. 2   5. 160
6. 8   7. 6   8. 16   9. 50   10. 1.4
11. 10   12. 12
Test 7
1. 19   2. 3   3. 11 tenths   4. 14
5. 12   6. 48   7. 4   8. 59   9. 11½
10. 20   11. 40   12. 0.9
Test 8
1. 13   2. 4   3. 2 thirds   4. 3½
5. 85   6. 8   7. 99   8. 13   9. 6
10. 42   11. 80   12. 8

Page 29 Time Yourself Tests
Test 9
1. 100   2. 2   3. 24   4. 34   5. 16
6. 6   7. 51   8. 4   9. 2   10. 14
11. 3.8   12. 15½
Test 10
1. 75   2. 2   3. 888   4. 45   5. 5.1
6. 38   7. 30   8. 84   9. 12   10. 48
11. 47   12. 19½
Test 11
1. 12½   2. 33   3. 209   4. 27   5. 13
6. 2   7. 22 quarters   8. 11   9. 17
10. 10   11. 5   12. 0.8
Test 12
1. 47   2. 13   3. 57   4. 44   5. 57
6. 28   7. 5½   8. 16   9. 39   10. 16
11. ¼   12. 78

Page 30 Time Yourself Tests
Test 13
1. 0.4   2. 90   3. 98   4. 31 sevenths
5. 397   6. 108   7. 90   8. 3 eighths
9. 2½   10. 20   11. £21.50   12. 35
Test 14
1. 909   2. 1026   3. 54   4. 74   5. 88
6. 3   7. 2¾   8. 56   9. 96   10. 54
11. 4¼   12. 78
Test 15
1. 34   2. 41   3. 30   4. 6   5. 24
6. 124   7. 46½   8. 41   9. 8998
10. 39   11. 96   12. 60
Test 16
1. 18 tenths   2. 6.3   3. 9   4. 8
5. 5   6. 3   7. 9 years   8. 264
9. 84   10. 3   11. 2.75   12. 70

Page 31 Time Yourself Tests
Test 17
1. £45.50   2. 12 fifths   3. 160
4. £1.70   5. 30   6. 39   7. 10   8. 67
9. 159   10. 97   11. 40 tenths   12. 97
Test 18
1. 140   2. 60   3. 100   4. 56
5. 40 082   6. 2100   7. 194   8. 30
9. 77 sevenths   10. 3   11. 4009   12. 29
Test 19
1. 42   2. 2   3. 56   4. 66   5. 12
6. 32   7. 10 halves   8. 7   9. 47
10. 99   11. 73   12. 88
Test 20
1. 11   2. 15 000   3. 0.8   4. 56   5. 7
6. 66   7. 129   8. 38½   9. 8.4
10. 99   11. 3849 centimetres   12. 1 half

Page 32 Time Yourself Tests
Test 21
1. 9   2. 26, 52   3. 6738   4. 24   5. 1
6. 795   7. 93   8. 78   9. 12.33
10. 650   11. 4400   12. 184
Test 22
1. 125   2. 60   3. 9.5   4. 14   5. 12
6. 59   7. 74   8. 76   9. 1.47   10. 64
11. ¹⁵⁄₅   12. 6
Test 23
1. 63   2. 75   3. 20   4. 9024   5. 56
6. 124   7. 7   8. 34   9. 59   10. 84
11. 44.5   12. 135
Test 24
1. 646   2. 94   3. 84   4. 20   5. 41
6. 140   7. 750, 590   8. 43½   9. 13
10. 93   11. 10   12. 51

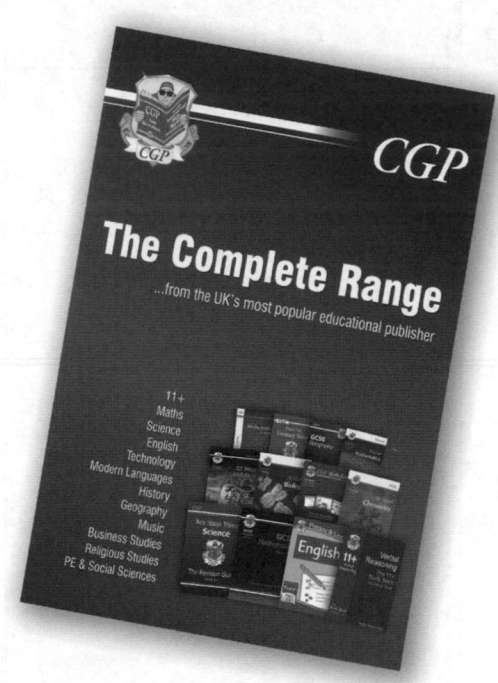